INLAND WATERWAYS

LOGBOOK

Contents

Introduction

One of the great delights of boating is looking back over previous trips and holidays, and planning new ones. Reliving favourite moments and occasional dramas, remembering best-loved stretches of water, the places you passed, and new friends you met on the way. It's what keeps us going through the winter, and it's the stories we swap with our fellow boaters.

This logbook will help you keep a record of the time you spend on board. It will also be an important help to the safe and reliable running of your craft. All the essential data and specifications of all the major items of equipment can be noted down, for future reference, maintenance and repair.

We have included a helpful section of useful information for when you are cruising. The experienced skipper will know most of this, but newcomers will find it a valuable aid. Also included is a simple map of the UK waterways, with basic information on all the navigable rivers and canals, to help you plan your next trip.

Happy cruising!

Emrhys Barrell
Goring-on-Thames

Boat Data

Name of boat

Previous names

Owner

Registered Number

Craft Identification Number (CIN)

Builder

Make of boat/type

Address

Tel   Email

Broker /Dealer

Address

Tel   Email

Insurance

Policy Number

Tel   Email

Breakdown cover

Policy Number

Tel   Email

Dimensions

Length overall	(ft)	(in)	(m)
Hull length	(ft)	(in)	(m)
Waterline length	(ft)	(in)	(m)
Beam overall	(ft)	(in)	(m)
Draft	(ft)	(in)	(m)
Air draft (Mast up)	(ft)	(in)	(m)
Air draft (Mast down)	(ft)	(in)	(m)
Weight	(kg)		
Engine fuel capacity	(gal)	(lt)	
Generator fuel capacity	(gal)	(lt)	
Water capacity	(gal)	(lt)	
Holding tank	(gal)	(lt)	

Engines

Make/model	Serial No(s)	
Power	(bhp)	Capacity	(lt)
No. cylinders	RPM	

Gearbox

Make/model	Ratio	Serial No(s)

Alternator 1

Make	Model
Volts	Amps

Alternator 2

Make	Model
Volts	Amps

Coupling
Stern gland
Stern bearing
Shaft

Diameter	(in/mm) Length	(in/mm) Material	

Propeller

Diameter	(in) Pitch	(in) Blades	RH/LH

Alternator drive belt 1

Length	Width	Type

Alternator drive belt 2

Length	Width	Type

Fuel filter   Oil filter

Engine oil	Quantity	(lt)
Gearbox oil	Quantity	(lt)

Engine/Gear controls

Type	Cable lengths	(ft/mm)	(ft/mm)

Paint

Cabin	Deck
Hull	Bottom

Anodes   Make/size

Equipment

Generator	Serial No
Heater	Serial No
Water pump	Serial No
Inverter	Serial No
Charger	Serial No
Cooker	Serial No
Fridge	Serial No
Microwave	Serial No
Dishwasher	Serial No
Washing machine	Serial No
Other	

Parts of a Boat

Like most activities, boating has its own language and special terms. Some of these might seem archaic and unnecessary but they often describe things for which there are no equivalent terms ashore. In any case, learning them is part of the fun and gets the whole crew into the spirit of the activity.

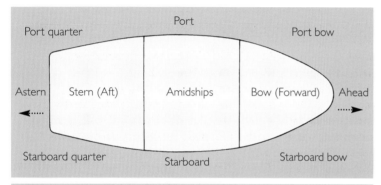

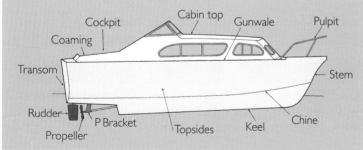

Parts of a typical cruiser.

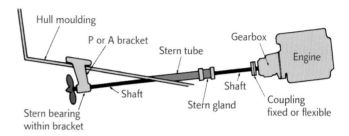

Engine arrangement on a cruiser.

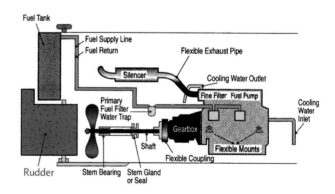

Engine arrangement on a narrowboat.

Nautical terms

Port and starboard Port is the left side and starboard is the right side when you are looking towards the bow. These terms also describe direction – 'I am turning to port' meaning 'I am turning the boat to the left'.

Forward and aft The front and rear halves of the boat, and also items found there – 'the forward cabin', 'the aft cabin' etc.

Bow and stern The bow is the forward part of a vessel while the stern is the part at the back.

Transom The flat surface across the stern of some boats.

Midships or amidships The centre of the boat, either in the fore-and-aft sense, or side-to-side. Also the relative position of the helm steering – 'the helm is amidships' meaning it is in its central position.

Ahead and astern These describe directions of movement – 'the boat was moving ahead', 'the boat was moving astern'. They also describe positions of objects or other boats relative to your craft – 'we could see the lock ahead', 'the other boat was astern'.

Abeam The position of objects or other craft on either side of your boat.

Length overall (LOA) The total length of the boat. including bathing platform and anchor platform if any.

Hull The main body of a boat excluding superstructure and masts.

Hull length The length of the hull only, excluding platforms or projections.

Waterline length The length of the hull at the waterline.

Beam overall Width at the widest part.

Draught (sometimes spelt draft) The maximum underwater depth of the boat.

Air draught The vertical distance from the waterline to the highest point of the boat. Used to estimate whether it can pass under a bridge.

Keel The lowest part of the bottom of the boat. Either the V-shape where the bottom sections meet or an extension below this.

Topsides The sides of the hull above the waterline.

Bottom The immersed part of the hull.

Chine The corner between bottom and sides.

Gunwale The corner between the deck and the topsides.

Cockpit An open-air part of the boat, protected by a raised coaming. It can be located forward, midships or aft. In the last two cases it may also include a helm position.

Displacement The weight of the boat.

Rudder Underwater plate that steers the boat.

Tiller Steering arm attached directly to the top of the rudder stock.

Wheel Steering wheel attached remotely to the rudder stock.

Helm Another word for the wheel, though it can also generally describe the steering system, either wheel or tiller.

Knots The speed of the boat, usually when describing sea-going craft. The speed of inland vessels is normally described in miles per hour; 1 knot equals 1.15mph.

Before you start off you should adopt the same approach as a pilot does before take-off:

- Flight plan
- Cockpit check
- Crew instructions

Flight plan Decide where you are going, and ensure the boat has everything for the trip. Check gas bottle, fuel and water, windlasses, maps and keys, toolkit and spares. It is worth making a list of all items you think you will need (such as dinghy, outboard, wellingtons etc). If you add to this list every time you forget something, it will end up covering everything.

Cockpit check Check engine oil and water. Open inlet cooling valve if fitted. Grease the stern gland. Start the engine and warm it up. Check oil pressure, temperature, cooling water, ammeter and volts. Clear any weed or debris from round the prop. Check the gears before casting off. Check the steering. Check the boathook, pole and plank are securely in place. Check the anchor is free and ready for use. Check the lifebuoy is ready to hand. Clear loose items from roof. Check fenders are attached. Secure the canopy. Coil ropes. Loosen mooring pins and lines.

Check the depth of water under the boat. Water levels on rivers and canals can drop overnight, leaving you stuck on the botttom, or with your rudder or prop in the mud. Rock the boat to check that it moves, and if in doubt ease the stern out from the bank with a boathook or pole before engaging gear.

Briefing the crew Now you are nearly ready to cast off. Before you do this, though, work out the best way of leaving your berth, taking into account wind and current, and then talk this plan through with the crew. Don't rely on telepathy or what seems obvious to you. If you are with your regular crew they will be familiar with the way you operate but even so, a short discussion on the bankside or in the cockpit will save arm-waving, shouting and confusion later.

If you have new crew members on board, explain what is expected of them and work out a simple system of signals. Once the engine is running it is often difficult to make yourself heard, particularly between helm and foredeck on a long boat; raised voices immediately attract the attention of onlookers and increase the tension on board.

A simple system of signals can be:

'Ready to let go' – from the crew – usually a thumbs-up.
'Let go' – from the helmsman – also a thumbs-up.
'Hold it as you are' – from either party – a raised hand.
'Come ahead' – from the crew – beckoning hand.
'Go astern' – from the crew – points astern.
'Push out' – from the helmsman – points away from bank.
'Pull in' – from the helmsman – points towards the bank.

How a Boat Steers

Because it often has a wheel, you may think a boat steers the same as a car, but the opposite is the case. Instead of the steering operating on the front wheels, it acts on the rudder at the stern. The effect is therefore similar to reversing your car. As you turn the wheel or move the tiller to turn to port, the bow swings to port, but the stern swings out to starboard, in the same way that the front of your car swings out into the road when you are reversing into a parking space. So be prepared for this swing when turning, and always watch your stern when close to the bank or other boats.

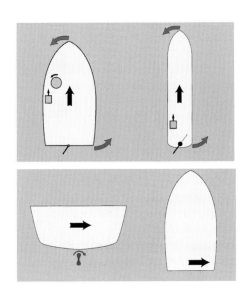

In addition, with a single-propeller boat, you have an effect called the paddle-wheel effect. This is caused by the rotation of the propeller, and at slow speeds it will kick the stern of the boat out. Most boats have a right-hand propeller, in which case the paddlewheel effect moves the stern to starboard when you go ahead, and to port when you go astern. (With a left-hand prop the movements are reversed.

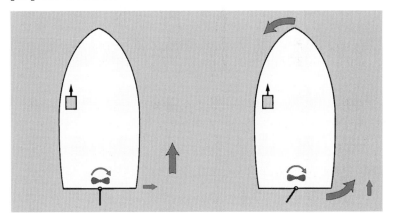

Above (left) the helm is amidships, the boat is stationary and the engine is put into ahead. A right-hand prop will give the stern a kick to starboard before the boat gathers way. On the right, the boat is also stationary and the engine is put into ahead, this time with the helm to port. The thrust of water from the propeller over the rudder will push the stern to starboard, and the bow will follow to port. The paddle-wheel effect increases the swing with a right-hand prop, and decreases it with a left-hand prop.

Rule of the Road

The rule of the waterways says you travel on the right. This applies to all waterways, in all countries of the world, and out at sea. In practice you do not have to drive right over by the bank – that will just annoy fishermen and owners of moored craft unnecessarily – but you should keep to the right of the centreline, particularly when meeting oncoming vessels. Be careful not to cut corners – it is easy to let your attention wander on a long bend and suddenly find yourself facing an oncoming boat!

The rule also says that overtaking boats must give way. If you have to overtake another craft, remember that its helmsman may not be aware of your presence. Wait till you have a straight stretch ahead of you, then pass with as much clearance as possible, without unduly impeding oncoming craft. Try to wait until the boat ahead is aware of your presence and can move over to let you past, though do not force him to pass too close to the bank. Similarly, if you are aware that a faster craft is coming up behind you, move over and call it past at the appropriate moment.

On some rivers and larger canals you may encounter large commercial vessels. These can range from passenger trip boats to tugs, barges and ferries. The rule say you should keep clear of these at all times. They will be less manoeuvrable than you in narrow waterways, and may be restricted by their draught. Be aware that they may have to travel down the centre of the channel, or even on the outside of some bends, to have enough deep water. If you are in doubt, pull over out of their way. When doing this, signal your intent, with one of the approved sound signals.

Official sound signals

The officially correct signals when manoeuvring are as follows:

1 short blast of the horn – I am altering course to starboard
2 short blasts of the horn – I am altering course to port
3 short blasts of the horn – My engines are in astern
5 short rapid blasts – I am uncertain of your actions
4 short blasts followed by 1 short blast – I am turning right round to starboard
4 short blasts followed by 2 short blasts – I am turning right round to port

Approved sound signals vary from waterway to waterway, but the first four are universal. The last two are used on the Thames, but understood elsewhere. Signals for European waterways are covered by international regulations.

In practice, when manoeuvring at slow speeds at close quarters, if you know the skipper of another boat is watching what you are doing, a simple hand signal will often suffice. But if you are in any doubt, use your horn.

Sailing dinghies can be unpredictable. Running with the wind behind them, they should keep to the correct side of the river. When tacking against the wind, they will have to make a turn every time they approach the bank, and you should slow down and pass behind them after they have turned. They are not allowed to make a sudden turn in front of you just to gain a racing advantage. The blanket rule that power always gives way to sail went out with the Onedin Line, but some helmsmen will still try it on.

Ropes

Boats on rivers are constantly tied up and cast off, so you should always look after your ropes. It is sometimes assumed that man-made fibres will last forever, but they all harden with age and exposure to ultra violet light, becoming difficult to handle and losing their strength. Take them home every winter and wash them through with warm soapy water to remove grit. Discard ropes with cut or frayed sections, as they will inevitably break at a critical moment. Any knots in the line will get tighter, making them impossible to undo, and will jam when pulled quickly around a cleat or ring.

Make up a set of separate lines at the same length as your permanent mooring ropes. This will enable you to keep your travelling lines clean, soft and strong.

Rope comes in various types and specifications. The three materials most commonly used are nylon, polyester and polypropylene, and each has its own benefits and disadvantages.

Nylon

Nylon is the strongest material. It also stretches the most. This might appear a disadvantage but, in fact, it gives it greater shock-absorbing properties which is useful for a mooring rope. It is available in either three-strand, braided or plaited forms, and is usually only available in white. It will tend to harden with age and exposure to sunlight.

Polyester

Polyester is almost as strong as nylon but it has far less stretch. It can be supplied in either three-strand or braided forms and is also available prestretched. It is mainly used for halyards and sheets on sailing boats, where resistance to stretch is essential. However, in its matt finish braided form, it is good to handle and therefore especially suitable for mooring lines which are used frequently. For this use, buy the non prestretched forms.

It remains softer and better to handle with age than nylon.

Polypropylene

Polypropylene is the cheapest. It is also the weakest of the three. It is usually blue in colour, though sometimes a natural colour today, and comes in three-strand form only. Its one advantage is that it floats. It hardens rapidly with age and exposure to the sun and when it does, the strands start to break and fray. They then form sharp, hard splinters which can cause painful injuries to your hands. It is popular with hireboat companies because of its price, and because of its buoyancy it is less likely to be sucked into the propeller if left hanging over the side when the boat is underway. However, it's not recommended for the private owner except possibly for permanent moorings for light craft or as a spare line.

Knots

Whole books are written on the subject of knots, but we recommend you and your crew practise and master these four main knots.

The **round turn and two half hitches** is the best mooring knot. It can be used to tie a rope to a post, pin or ring. It is secure, but can be easily released even under load. Always remember to go twice round the post, then tie two half hitches.

The **bowline** is used to make a secure loop in the end of a rope, that will not tighten or slip, but also can be easily released when the load is taken off. For this reason it is the only knot used by climbers for tying a rope round themselves. Use it to make a loop in the end of a mooring rope that can be slipped over a bollard or post. It can also be used to join two lengths of rope together, with one tied through the other. It is a difficult knot to tie correctly, so practice it frequently.

The **reef knot** can be used to tie two lightly-loaded cords together, but in practice is best reserved for parcels and shoe-laces.

The **clove hitch** can be used for tying fenders to a rail, but it can unwind, so should be secured with a half hitch.

Round turn and two half hitches

Bowline

Reef knot

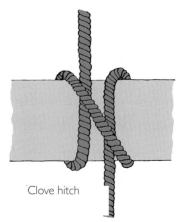

Clove hitch

Locks, Bridges and Tunnels

- Locks come in many different types and sizes. The diagrams to the right show a lock on a narrow beam canal, which is similar in principle to all others.
- Your boat must be fitted with a spotlight or headlight forward, and when in a tunnel this must be on at all times. Do not aim it straight ahead, as it will be ineffective and dazzle an oncoming boat. Instead, angle it down and to the right, shining slightly ahead of the boat.
- Make sure you have a powerful torch handy, in case you need to pick anything out. Do not show a bright light at the stern, as this will confuse boats following behind.
- Before entering the tunnel, turn some lights on in the cabin and open the curtains; light will then shine through the windows on to the tunnel wall, making it easier to hold your position in the centre of the channel. Do not let the lights shine directly at the helmsman.
- Clear all loose items off the roof before entering, and fold down any windscreens. Crew should be safely in the cabin or cockpit. Check engine temperature, oil pressure, cooling water and fuel gauge before entering a tunnel. Extinguish all naked flames – cookers and heaters.
- Tunnels are wet places so put on waterproofs.
- Few narrow tunnels have a traffic light system or set times for passage in either direction, so as you approach, look ahead for the lights of oncoming craft. It is quite acceptable to follow another boat through, unless you have passed any allotted time for entering.

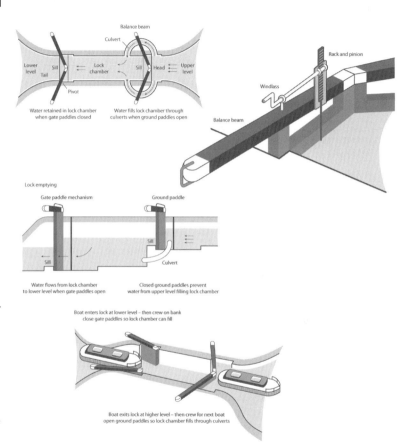

Balance beam
Culvert
Lower level
Sill
Tail
Lock chamber
Sill
Head
Upper level
Pivot

Water retained in lock chamber when gate paddles closed

Water fills lock chamber through culverts when ground paddles open

Balance beam

Rack and pinion

Windlass

Lock emptying

Gate paddle mechanism

Ground paddle

Sill

Sill

Culvert

Water flows from lock chamber to lower level when gate paddles open

Closed ground paddles prevent water from upper level filling lock chamber

Boat enters lock at lower level – then crew on bank close gate paddles so lock chamber can fill

Boat exits lock at higher level – then crew for next boat open ground paddles so lock chamber fills through culverts

Man Overboard

If you or one of your crew fall off your boat, it will usually just be inconvenient, wet and amusing. Sometimes, however, life could be at risk. It is essential therefore that everyone aboard knows what to do in this situation.

• If someone falls off the boat shout 'man overboard'. Never mind how dramatic or hackneyed this sounds, it will be instantly understood.

• Immediately put the engine into neutral to stop the boat and prevent injury to the person in the water from the propeller.

• As soon as the victim is located, throw a lifebuoy to them. Point continuously at the victim so that you don't lose sight of them, calling out their position to the helmsman.

• Once the victim has reached the belt, you can set about recovering them. By this time they will probably be astern. Do not reverse up to them or you will risk injuring them with the propeller. Motor ahead and turn, coming up to the victim from downwind or downstream. On a narrow canal it will not be possible to turn so you will have to reverse very carefully.

• If they have been injured when going overboard and are unconscious or unable to help themselves, consider putting an able-bodied adult over the side, with a lifejacket on, to help them, but only if this does not deplete the crew on board. At all times reassure the casualty.

• If you have enough strong people on board to lift the casualty, then do so. Otherwise launch the tender or hail a smaller passing boat. Or drive your boat slowly towards the bank following the casualty (at the bow) so that they can scramble ashore if they are able.

• If someone falls into a lock, this calls for different actions. If the lock is filling or emptying, the first priority is to drop all the paddles. At the same time, ensure that the boat does not crush the victim against the gate or wall. A lifebuoy will give some protection but you should quickly drop extra fenders in the gap on the other side of the boat or the large round fender that many boats have near the bow.

• Once the water flow has stabilised, it is often very difficult to get the victim back on board; it may be easiest to shepherd them to the ladder or steps. If they are injured or distressed, an adult should go in with them, wearing a lifejacket. In a part-filled narrow lock where the boat is blocking access to the steps and you cannot recover the casualty, secure them with a rope, let the remainder of the water slowly out of the lock and drift the boat to the step outside the lock.

The best way to prepare yourself and your crew for a man-overboard situation is to practise it in advance. Use an inflated lifejacket as the victim and follow all the steps through – it is a worthwhile exercise that could save a life one day.

Maintenance and Laying Up

Proper maintenance of your boat, especially the engine, is essential for safe, trouble-free boating. Here are the main points you examine on a regular basis, or every winter.

Daily or weekly checks

Check the engine oil, cooling water level, stern-gland greaser, alternator belts.

Check the battery voltage and charging current, and electrolyte level.

Annual maintenance and laying-up

Change the engine oil and filter (preferably before the winter, or at the manufacturer's recommended interval).

Check for oil leaks under the engine.

Change or check the fuel filter.

Change or clean the air filter.

Check fuel lines for leaks.

Check cooling water anti-freeze concentration (before winter).

Drain the cooling system on raw-water cooled engines.

Check the alternator belts for tension and fraying.

Check the engine mounting bolts and coupling bolts.

Check the gearbox oil level. Change at manufacturer's recommended interval.

Re-pack the stern greaser.

Check the bilge pump operation.

Fill the fuel tank to prevent condensation.

Clean the terminals and tops, charge the batteries fully.

Drain the domestic freshwater system to prevent freezing.

Sterilise the tanks with a proprietary cleaner.

Check the gas bottle stowage. Turn off the gas.

Empty the fridge. Leave the door propped open.

Remove all perishable foods (biscuits etc) which could attract animals.

Leave ventilators open, plus internal doors, drawers and cupboards to prevent condensation and mould.

Remove cushions, or stand them on edge.

Take wet weather gear home.

Check lifejackets.

Remove loose items from the roof

Check all ropes for cuts or fraying. Undo any knots in them.

Take ropes home and clean thoroughly by soaking overnight in warm, soapy water. Dry them before storing.

Hull

Touch up damaged paintwork above the waterline.

Check anodes. Replace every 2-3 years.

Repaint the bottom every 2-3 years.

Check hull for damage.

Check prop, rudder, shaft and stern bearing.

Weil's Disease

Weil's Disease (or leptospirosis) is a rare but potentially extremely dangerous bacterial infection that can attack anyone who comes into contact with stagnant water or soil. It is carried in the urine of infected animals, which can include cattle, pigs, horses, dogs, wild animals and rats. It gets into the human bloodstream mainly through the skin, particularly through cuts or open wounds. Symptoms include severe headache, fever, chills, muscle ache, nausea, abdominal pain, and diarrhea. The onset of symptoms can be anything between two days and four weeks from exposure, but is typically 3-14 days. Often the symptoms go away after a few days, but then recur. If it is untreated it can attack the kidneys, liver and immune system, quickly leading to partial paralysis or even death.

Because the symptoms are similar to flu, it can be disregarded by the victim or the medical profession, but if you experience the symptoms, see a doctor and stress that you have been in contact with stagnant water. They can check for the disease with a blood test.

Precautions include always wearing long rubber gloves when working underwater (when clearing the prop for instance), covering cuts with plasters at all times when you are on board, and washing your hands after handling ropes that have been in the water. For more information go to: www.leptospirosis.org

Security

We all go boating to get away from the cares of modern life, but in today's society crime is everywhere, and you should still take simple precautions to prevent it spoiling your holiday.

When leaving your boat, even for short periods, clear all valuables, tools, radios and phones out of sight, to remove temptation. Over winter you should take them home with you, along with any drink – don't give the thieves an excuse for a party on your boat.

Items of equipment should be marked with your postcode. Scratch this on the back, and add it again in invisible ink in a hidden place. Even when police recover stolen property, it is amazing how much cannot be identified, and has to be sold off at auctions. Make a note of the serial numbers for your insurance, and keep a copy of the receipts. If you are going to boat jumbles or car boot sales, be very careful before buying anything you are unsure of.

When going ashore for the evening, close the curtains and leave on a cabin light and the radio. Tie the mooring lines round the ring or pin ashore, then take the end back onto the boat. Just this little difference might prevent the casual vandals from casting your boat adrift. Take loose items off the roof and out of the cockpit. If you are really concerned about the spot you have chosen, discreetly lower the anchor over the side of the boat away from the bank to prevent your craft drifting away.

Burglar alarms can help, and some will ring your mobile phone if your boat is broken into, though whether you want to be woken at home in the middle of the night when a stray cat jumps aboard is another matter.

Avoid leaving any details on board that can identify you or where you live. For this reason we advise that you don't put your name and address in the front of this log, or the addresses of guests who may come on board. The same applies to painting your names and home town on the side of your craft. The smart thief will work out that your home is empty when you are on the boat.

Map of the Inland Waterways

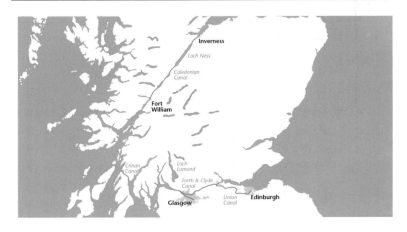

This information was accurate at the time of going to press, but you are advised to ring to check before travelling

Length in miles	Number of locks	Max dimensions of vessel LOA, beam & draft	Max height of vessel above water	Length in miles	Number of locks	Max dimensions of vessel LOA, beam & draft	Max height of vessel above water
Aire & Calder Navigation Tel: 01977 554351				**River Derwent** Tel: 01904 659570			
41	17	140ft x17ft 8in x 6ft10in	12ft 2in	21	2	55ft x 14ft x 6 –10ft	4ft
River Ancholme Tel: 01522 512927				**Exeter Ship Canal** Tel: 01392 74306			
19	11	50ft x12ft x 3–6 ft	11ft 6in	5	2	122ft x 25ft x 10ft 6in	No limit
Ashby Canal Tel: 01288 790236				**Fossdyke & Witham Canal** Tel: 01636 704481			
22	11	70ft x 7ft x 2ft 6in	6ft 6in	45	4	74ft 6in x 15ft 2in x 5ft	8ft 10in
Ashton Canal Tel: 0161819 5847				**Gloucester & Sharpness Canal** Tel: 01452 319000			
6	18	70ft x 7ft x 2ft 9in	6ft 9in	17	2	144ft x 22ft x 10ft	No limit
River Avon Tel: 01386 552517				**Grand Union Canal** Tel: 0121 5061300 Nth. 01908 302500 Cen. 0207 9857780 Sth.			
44	17	70ft x 12ft 6in x 3ft	6ft.	137 + 42m **Leicester** + 35m **Northants**,			
Basingstoke Canal Tel: 01252 370073				Total **250**		70ft x 12ft 6in x 3ft 6in	7ft (Leicester)
31	29	70ft x 13ft 6in x 2ft 6in	6-9ft.				7ft. (Northants)
Birmingham Canal Navigations Tel: 0121 506 1300				**Grand Western Canal** Tel: 01392 77977			
120+	190	70ft x 7ft x 2ft 6in	6ft 6in	10	0	No limit x 7ft x 2ft 6in	7ft
Bridgewater Canal Tel: 0161 872 2411				**Huddersfield Narrow Canal**			
28	0	70ft x 14ft 9in x 4ft	11ft	40	74	70ft x 6ft 10in x 3ft 6in	6ft 2in
Bridgwater & Taunton Canal Tel: 01873 830328				**Huddersfield Broad Canal** Tel: 0161 819 5847			
14	6	50ft x 10ft x 3ft	6ft 6in	4	9	58ft 6in x 14ft 2in x 2ft 6in	9ft 6in
Calder & Hebble Navigation Tel: 01977 554351				**River Idle** Tel: 01543 444161			
21	39	57ft 6in x 14ft 2in x 3ft	9in 9ft	10	0	No limit x 18ft x 2ft 6in	9ft
River Cam Tel: 01223 58977				**Kennet & Avon Canal** Tel: 01380 722859			
14	3	100ft x 14ft x 4ft	9ft	86	86	72ft x 13ft 10in x 3ft	7ft
Chelmer & Blackwater Navigation Tel: 01245 222025				**Lancaster Canal** Tel: 01524 751888			
14	13	60ft x 16ft x 2ft	6ft	42 **01** + **Ribble Link,** 4 **9**		72ft x 14ft 6in x 3ft	8ft
Chesterfield Canal Tel: 01636 704481				**Rivers Lee & Stort** Tel: 01932 788375			
45	(31 rest) **651** (46 rest)	72ft x 7ft x 2ft 6in	7ft	40	36	86ft x 13ft 4in x 3ft	6ft
Coventry Canal Tel: 01283 790236				**Leeds & Liverpool Canal** Tel: 01274 611303			
38	13	70ft x 7ft x 2ft 6in	6ft 6in	127	9	62ft x 14ft x 3ft 6in	7ft 6in
River Dee Tel: 01295 653999				**Llangollen Canal** Tel: 01244 390372			
12	0	No limit x No limit x 3ft	10ft	46	21	70ft x 7ft x 2ft	2ft 3in

Length in miles	Number of locks	Max dimensions of vessel LOA, beam & draft	Max height of vessel above water
Macclesfield Canal	Tel: 01782 785703		
26	13	70ft x 7ft x 2ft 9in	6ft 6in
Manchester Ship Canal	Tel: 0151 327 1461		
26	4	600ft x 65ft x 30ft	70ft
River Medway	Tel: 01903 832000		
43	10	80ft x 18ft 6in x 4ft	8ft 6in
Middle Level Navigations	Tel: 01354 653232		
90	7	80ft x 11ft 6in x 2ft 3in	6-7ft
Monmouth & Brecon Canal	Tel: 01873 830328		
35	6	43ft x 8ft 6in x 2ft 6in	5ft 10in
River Nene	Tel: 01733 371811		
91	38	78ft x 13ft x 4ft	7ft
Norfolk & Suffolk Broads	Tel: 01603 610734		
125	0	No limit x 16ft x 3-5ft	6ft 6in
Great Ouse	Tel: 01733 371811		
85	16	70ft x 10ft 6in x 3ft 3in	7ft 6in
Yorkshire Ouse	Tel: 01904 728229		
70	5	60ft x 14ft 6in x 3-4ft	8ft 6in
Oxford Canal	Tel: 01788 890666		
77	46	70ft x 7ft x 3ft	7ft
Peak Forest Canal	Tel: 01782 785703		
15	16	70ft x 7ft x 2ft 9in	6ft
Regent's Canal (Part of Grand Union)			
Rochdale Canal	Tel: 01422 844990		
42	5	74ft x 14ft 2in x 4ft	9ft
River Soar to Leicester	Tel: 01636 704481		
36	22	70ft x 10ft 6in x 3ft	7ft 6in
River Severn	Tel: 01452 318000		
42	5	88ft x 18ft x 6ft	21ft
Sheffield & S Yorks Navigation	Tel: 01636 704481		
42	26	61ft x 15ft 3in x 4ft 6in	10ft
Shropshire Union	Tel: 01786 284253		
66	46	70ft x 7ft x 3ft 3in	8ft
Staffs & Worcs Canal	Tel: 01785 284253		
46	31	70ft x 7ft x 2ft 6in	6ft 3in
River Stour (Suffolk)	Tel: 01473 727712		
23	15	Restricted navigation. 50ft	10ft
Stourbridge Canal	Tel: 0121 506 1300		
6	20	70ft x 7ft x 2ft 6in	6ft
Stratford-Upon-Avon Canal	Tel: 01564 784634		
25	55	70ft x 7ft x 2ft 6in	6ft
River Thames	Tel: 01189 535000		
143	44	To Oxford 120ft x 17ft x 4ft	11ft
		Above Oxford: 109ft x 14ft x 3ft	7ft 6in
River Trent to Nottingham	Tel: 01636 704481		
81	7	145ft x 18ft 6in x 6ft	12ft 3in
Trent & Mersey Canal	Tel: 01283 790236		
93	76	70ft x 7ft x 2ft 6in	5ft 9in
River Wey	Tel: 01483 561389		
19	16	73ft 6in x 13ft 9in x 2ft 6in	7ft (6ft)
Worcester & Birmingham Canal	Tel: 01564 784634		
30	58	70ft x 7ft x 2ft 6in	6ft

Scotland (Tel: 0141 332 6936)

Length in miles	Number of locks	Max dimensions of vessel LOA, beam & draft	Max height of vessel above water
Caledonian Canal			
60	29	150ft x 35ft	
Forth & Clyde and Union Canals			
70	40	66ft x 19ft 8in	(11ft 3in)

Date/day

Waterway _____

From _____ To _____

Crew on board _____

Guests _____

Start time _____ Finish _____

Engine hours: _____

Start _____ Finish _____ Total ____

Fuel level _____ Water level _____

No of miles _____ No of locks _____

Weather _____

Waterway conditions _____

Purpose of journey _____

_____

_____

_____

_____

_____

Notes

Places passed _____

_____

_____

_____

_____

Other boats seen _____

_____

Wildlife seen _____

_____

Details of mooring _____

_____

_____

Jobs done _____

_____

Jobs to do _____

_____

Date/day

Waterway

From   To

Crew on board

Guests

Start time   Finish

Engine hours:

Start   Finish   Total

Fuel level   Water level

No of miles   No of locks

Weather

Waterway conditions

Purpose of journey

Notes

Places passed

Other boats seen

Wildlife seen

Details of mooring

Jobs done

Jobs to do

Date/day

Waterway

From .... To

Crew on board

Guests

Start time .... Finish

Engine hours:

Start .... Finish .... Total

Fuel level .... Water level

No of miles .... No of locks

Weather

Waterway conditions

Purpose of journey

Notes

Places passed

Other boats seen

Wildlife seen

Details of mooring

Jobs done

Jobs to do

Date/day

Waterway

From   To

Crew on board

Guests

Start time   Finish

Engine hours:

Start   Finish   Total

Fuel level   Water level

No of miles   No of locks

Weather

Waterway conditions

Purpose of journey

Notes

Places passed

Other boats seen

Wildlife seen

Details of mooring

Jobs done

Jobs to do

Date/day

Waterway

From   To

Crew on board

Guests

Start time   Finish

Engine hours:

Start   Finish   Total

Fuel level   Water level

No of miles   No of locks

Weather

Waterway conditions

Purpose of journey

Notes

Places passed

Other boats seen

Wildlife seen

Details of mooring

Jobs done

Jobs to do

Date/day

Waterway

From   To

Crew on board

Guests

Start time   Finish

Engine hours:

Start   Finish   Total

Fuel level   Water level

No of miles   No of locks

Weather

Waterway conditions

Purpose of journey

Notes

Places passed

Other boats seen

Wildlife seen

Details of mooring

Jobs done

Jobs to do

Date/day

Waterway

From   To

Crew on board

Guests

Start time   Finish

Engine hours:

Start   Finish   Total

Fuel level   Water level

No of miles   No of locks

Weather

Waterway conditions

Purpose of journey

Notes

Places passed

Other boats seen

Wildlife seen

Details of mooring

Jobs done

Jobs to do

Daily Pages

Date/day

Waterway

From   To

Crew on board

Guests

Start time   Finish

Engine hours:

Start   Finish   Total

Fuel level   Water level

No of miles   No of locks

Weather

Waterway conditions

Purpose of journey

Notes

Places passed

Other boats seen

Wildlife seen

Details of mooring

Jobs done

Jobs to do

Date/day

Waterway

From   To

Crew on board

Guests

Start time   Finish

Engine hours:

Start   Finish   Total

Fuel level   Water level

No of miles   No of locks

Weather

Waterway conditions

Purpose of journey

Notes

Places passed

Other boats seen

Wildlife seen

Details of mooring

Jobs done

Jobs to do

Date/day

Waterway

From   To

Crew on board

Guests

Start time   Finish

Engine hours:

Start   Finish   Total

Fuel level   Water level

No of miles   No of locks

Weather

Waterway conditions

Purpose of journey

Notes

Places passed

Other boats seen

Wildlife seen

Details of mooring

Jobs done

Jobs to do

Date/day

Waterway

From   To

Crew on board

Guests

Start time   Finish

Engine hours:

Start   Finish   Total

Fuel level   Water level

No of miles   No of locks

Weather

Waterway conditions

Purpose of journey

Notes

Places passed

Other boats seen

Wildlife seen

Details of mooring

Jobs done

Jobs to do

Daily Pages

Date/day

Waterway

From   To

Crew on board

Guests

Start time   Finish

Engine hours:

Start   Finish   Total

Fuel level   Water level

No of miles   No of locks

Weather

Waterway conditions

Purpose of journey

Notes

Places passed

Other boats seen

Wildlife seen

Details of mooring

Jobs done

Jobs to do

Daily Pages

Date/day

Waterway

From   To

Crew on board

Guests

Start time   Finish

Engine hours:

Start   Finish   Total

Fuel level   Water level

No of miles   No of locks

Weather

Waterway conditions

Purpose of journey

Notes

Places passed

Other boats seen

Wildlife seen

Details of mooring

Jobs done

Jobs to do

Date/day

Waterway

From   To

Crew on board

Guests

Start time   Finish

Engine hours:

Start   Finish   Total

Fuel level   Water level

No of miles   No of locks

Weather

Waterway conditions

Purpose of journey

Notes

Places passed

Other boats seen

Wildlife seen

Details of mooring

Jobs done

Jobs to do

Date/day

Waterway

From   To

Crew on board

Guests

Start time   Finish

Engine hours:

Start   Finish   Total

Fuel level   Water level

No of miles   No of locks

Weather

Waterway conditions

Purpose of journey

Notes

Places passed

Other boats seen

Wildlife seen

Details of mooring

Jobs done

Jobs to do

Date/day

Waterway

From   To

Crew on board

Guests

Start time   Finish

Engine hours:

Start   Finish   Total

Fuel level   Water level

No of miles   No of locks

Weather

Waterway conditions

Purpose of journey

Notes

Places passed

Other boats seen

Wildlife seen

Details of mooring

Jobs done

Jobs to do

Date/day

Waterway

From   To

Crew on board

Guests

Start time   Finish

Engine hours:

Start   Finish   Total

Fuel level   Water level

No of miles   No of locks

Weather

Waterway conditions

Purpose of journey

Notes

Places passed

Other boats seen

Wildlife seen

Details of mooring

Jobs done

Jobs to do

Daily Pages

Date/day

Waterway

From   To

Crew on board

Guests

Start time   Finish

Engine hours:

Start   Finish   Total

Fuel level   Water level

No of miles   No of locks

Weather

Waterway conditions

Purpose of journey

Notes

Places passed

Other boats seen

Wildlife seen

Details of mooring

Jobs done

Jobs to do

Date/day

Waterway

From   To

Crew on board

Guests

Start time   Finish

Engine hours:

Start   Finish   Total

Fuel level   Water level

No of miles   No of locks

Weather

Waterway conditions

Purpose of journey

Notes

Places passed

Other boats seen

Wildlife seen

Details of mooring

Jobs done

Jobs to do

Daily Pages

Date/day

Waterway

From   To

Crew on board

Guests

Start time   Finish

Engine hours:

Start   Finish   Total

Fuel level   Water level

No of miles   No of locks

Weather

Waterway conditions

Purpose of journey

Notes

Places passed

Other boats seen

Wildlife seen

Details of mooring

Jobs done

Jobs to do

Date/day

Waterway _____

From _____ To _____

Crew on board _____

Guests _____

Start time _____ Finish _____

Engine hours:

Start _____ Finish _____ Total _____

Fuel level _____ Water level _____

No of miles _____ No of locks _____

Weather _____

Waterway conditions _____

Purpose of journey _____

_____

_____

_____

_____

_____

Notes

Places passed _____

_____

_____

_____

Other boats seen _____

_____

Wildlife seen _____

_____

Details of mooring _____

_____

Jobs done _____

Jobs to do _____

_____

Date/day

Waterway

From   To

Crew on board

Guests

Start time   Finish

Engine hours:

Start   Finish   Total

Fuel level   Water level

No of miles   No of locks

Weather

Waterway conditions

Purpose of journey

Notes

Places passed

Other boats seen

Wildlife seen

Details of mooring

Jobs done

Jobs to do

Date/day

Waterway

From   To

Crew on board

Guests

Start time   Finish

Engine hours:

Start   Finish   Total

Fuel level   Water level

No of miles   No of locks

Weather

Waterway conditions

Purpose of journey

Notes

Places passed

Other boats seen

Wildlife seen

Details of mooring

Jobs done

Jobs to do

Daily Pages

Date/day

Waterway

From   To

Crew on board

Guests

Start time   Finish

Engine hours:

Start   Finish   Total

Fuel level   Water level

No of miles   No of locks

Weather

Waterway conditions

Purpose of journey

Notes

Places passed

Other boats seen

Wildlife seen

Details of mooring

Jobs done

Jobs to do

Date/day

Waterway

From   To

Crew on board

Guests

Start time   Finish

Engine hours:

Start   Finish   Total

Fuel level   Water level

No of miles   No of locks

Weather

Waterway conditions

Purpose of journey

Notes

Places passed

Other boats seen

Wildlife seen

Details of mooring

Jobs done

Jobs to do

Daily Pages

Date/day

Waterway

From   To

Crew on board

Guests

Start time   Finish

Engine hours:

Start   Finish   Total

Fuel level   Water level

No of miles   No of locks

Weather

Waterway conditions

Purpose of journey

Notes

Places passed

Other boats seen

Wildlife seen

Details of mooring

Jobs done

Jobs to do

Date/day

Waterway

From   To

Crew on board

Guests

Start time   Finish

Engine hours:

Start   Finish   Total

Fuel level   Water level

No of miles   No of locks

Weather

Waterway conditions

Purpose of journey

Notes

Places passed

Other boats seen

Wildlife seen

Details of mooring

Jobs done

Jobs to do

Date/day

Waterway

From   To

Crew on board

Guests

Start time   Finish

Engine hours:

Start   Finish   Total

Fuel level   Water level

No of miles   No of locks

Weather

Waterway conditions

Purpose of journey

Notes

Places passed

Other boats seen

Wildlife seen

Details of mooring

Jobs done

Jobs to do

Daily Pages

Date/day

Waterway

From   To

Crew on board

Guests

Start time   Finish

Engine hours:

Start   Finish   Total

Fuel level   Water level

No of miles   No of locks

Weather

Waterway conditions

Purpose of journey

Notes

Places passed

Other boats seen

Wildlife seen

Details of mooring

Jobs done

Jobs to do

Date/day

Waterway

From   To

Crew on board

Guests

Start time   Finish

Engine hours:

Start   Finish   Total

Fuel level   Water level

No of miles   No of locks

Weather

Waterway conditions

Purpose of journey

Notes

Places passed

Other boats seen

Wildlife seen

Details of mooring

Jobs done

Jobs to do

Date/day

Waterway

From   To

Crew on board

Guests

Start time   Finish

Engine hours:

Start   Finish   Total

Fuel level   Water level

No of miles   No of locks

Weather

Waterway conditions

Purpose of journey

Notes

Places passed

Other boats seen

Wildlife seen

Details of mooring

Jobs done

Jobs to do

Date/day

Waterway

From   To

Crew on board

Guests

Start time   Finish

Engine hours:

Start   Finish   Total

Fuel level   Water level

No of miles   No of locks

Weather

Waterway conditions

Purpose of journey

Notes

Places passed

Other boats seen

Wildlife seen

Details of mooring

Jobs done

Jobs to do

Date/day

Waterway

From   To

Crew on board

Guests

Start time   Finish

Engine hours:

Start   Finish   Total

Fuel level   Water level

No of miles   No of locks

Weather

Waterway conditions

Purpose of journey

Notes

Places passed

Other boats seen

Wildlife seen

Details of mooring

Jobs done

Jobs to do

Date/day

Waterway

From   To

Crew on board

Guests

Start time   Finish

Engine hours:

Start   Finish   Total

Fuel level   Water level

No of miles   No of locks

Weather

Waterway conditions

Purpose of journey

Notes

Places passed

Other boats seen

Wildlife seen

Details of mooring

Jobs done

Jobs to do

Date/day

Waterway

From   To

Crew on board

Guests

Start time   Finish

Engine hours:

Start   Finish   Total

Fuel level   Water level

No of miles   No of locks

Weather

Waterway conditions

Purpose of journey

Notes

Places passed

Other boats seen

Wildlife seen

Details of mooring

Jobs done

Jobs to do

Daily Pages

Date/day

Waterway

From   To

Crew on board

Guests

Start time   Finish

Engine hours:

Start   Finish   Total

Fuel level   Water level

No of miles   No of locks

Weather

Waterway conditions

Purpose of journey

Notes

Places passed

Other boats seen

Wildlife seen

Details of mooring

Jobs done

Jobs to do

Date/day

Waterway

From   To

Crew on board

Guests

Start time   Finish

Engine hours:

Start   Finish   Total

Fuel level   Water level

No of miles   No of locks

Weather

Waterway conditions

Purpose of journey

Notes

Places passed

Other boats seen

Wildlife seen

Details of mooring

Jobs done

Jobs to do

Date/day

Waterway

From   To

Crew on board

Guests

Start time   Finish

Engine hours:

Start   Finish   Total

Fuel level   Water level

No of miles   No of locks

Weather

Waterway conditions

Purpose of journey

Notes

Places passed

Other boats seen

Wildlife seen

Details of mooring

Jobs done

Jobs to do

Date/day

Waterway

From   To

Crew on board

Guests

Start time   Finish

Engine hours:

Start   Finish   Total

Fuel level   Water level

No of miles   No of locks

Weather

Waterway conditions

Purpose of journey

Notes

Places passed

Other boats seen

Wildlife seen

Details of mooring

Jobs done

Jobs to do

Date/day

Waterway

From   To

Crew on board

Guests

Start time   Finish

Engine hours:

Start   Finish   Total

Fuel level   Water level

No of miles   No of locks

Weather

Waterway conditions

Purpose of journey

Notes

Places passed

Other boats seen

Wildlife seen

Details of mooring

Jobs done

Jobs to do

Date/day

Waterway

From   To

Crew on board

Guests

Start time   Finish

Engine hours:

Start   Finish   Total

Fuel level   Water level

No of miles   No of locks

Weather

Waterway conditions

Purpose of journey

Notes

Places passed

Other boats seen

Wildlife seen

Details of mooring

Jobs done

Jobs to do

Daily Pages

Date/day

Waterway

From   To

Crew on board

Guests

Start time   Finish

Engine hours:

Start   Finish   Total

Fuel level   Water level

No of miles   No of locks

Weather

Waterway conditions

Purpose of journey

Notes

Places passed

Other boats seen

Wildlife seen

Details of mooring

Jobs done

Jobs to do

Date/day

Waterway

From   To

Crew on board

Guests

Start time   Finish

Engine hours:

Start   Finish   Total

Fuel level   Water level

No of miles   No of locks

Weather

Waterway conditions

Purpose of journey

Notes

Places passed

Other boats seen

Wildlife seen

Details of mooring

Jobs done

Jobs to do

Daily Pages

Date/day

Waterway

From   To

Crew on board

Guests

Start time   Finish

Engine hours:

Start   Finish   Total

Fuel level   Water level

No of miles   No of locks

Weather

Waterway conditions

Purpose of journey

Notes

Places passed

Other boats seen

Wildlife seen

Details of mooring

Jobs done

Jobs to do

Date/day

Waterway _____

From _____ To _____

Crew on board _____

Guests _____

Start time _____ Finish _____

Engine hours: _____

Start _____ Finish _____ Total ____

Fuel level _____ Water level _____

No of miles _____ No of locks _____

Weather _____

Waterway conditions _____

Purpose of journey _____

_____

_____

_____

_____

_____

Notes

Places passed _____

_____

_____

_____

_____

Other boats seen _____

_____

Wildlife seen _____

_____

_____

_____

Details of mooring _____

_____

_____

Jobs done _____

_____

Jobs to do _____

_____

_____

Date/day

Waterway

From   To

Crew on board

Guests

Start time   Finish

Engine hours:

Start   Finish   Total

Fuel level   Water level

No of miles   No of locks

Weather

Waterway conditions

Purpose of journey

Notes

Places passed

Other boats seen

Wildlife seen

Details of mooring

Jobs done

Jobs to do

Daily Pages

Date/day

Waterway

From   To

Crew on board

Guests

Start time   Finish

Engine hours:

Start   Finish   Total

Fuel level   Water level

No of miles   No of locks

Weather

Waterway conditions

Purpose of journey

Notes

Places passed

Other boats seen

Wildlife seen

Details of mooring

Jobs done

Jobs to do

Daily Pages

Date/day

Waterway

From   To

Crew on board

Guests

Start time   Finish

Engine hours:

Start   Finish   Total

Fuel level   Water level

No of miles   No of locks

Weather

Waterway conditions

Purpose of journey

Notes

Places passed

Other boats seen

Wildlife seen

Details of mooring

Jobs done

Jobs to do

Date/day

Waterway

From   To

Crew on board

Guests

Start time   Finish

Engine hours:

Start   Finish   Total

Fuel level   Water level

No of miles   No of locks

Weather

Waterway conditions

Purpose of journey

Notes

Places passed

Other boats seen

Wildlife seen

Details of mooring

Jobs done

Jobs to do

Date/day

Waterway

From   To

Crew on board

Guests

Start time   Finish

Engine hours:

Start   Finish   Total

Fuel level   Water level

No of miles   No of locks

Weather

Waterway conditions

Purpose of journey

Notes

Places passed

Other boats seen

Wildlife seen

Details of mooring

Jobs done

Jobs to do

Date/day

Waterway

From   To

Crew on board

Guests

Start time   Finish

Engine hours:

Start   Finish   Total

Fuel level   Water level

No of miles   No of locks

Weather

Waterway conditions

Purpose of journey

Notes

Places passed

Other boats seen

Wildlife seen

Details of mooring

Jobs done

Jobs to do

Date/day

Waterway

From   To

Crew on board

Guests

Start time   Finish

Engine hours:

Start   Finish   Total

Fuel level   Water level

No of miles   No of locks

Weather

Waterway conditions

Purpose of journey

Notes

Places passed

Other boats seen

Wildlife seen

Details of mooring

Jobs done

Jobs to do

Date/day

Waterway

From   To

Crew on board

Guests

Start time   Finish

Engine hours:

Start   Finish   Total

Fuel level   Water level

No of miles   No of locks

Weather

Waterway conditions

Purpose of journey

Notes

Places passed

Other boats seen

Wildlife seen

Details of mooring

Jobs done

Jobs to do

Daily Pages

Date/day

Waterway

From   To

Crew on board

Guests

Start time   Finish

Engine hours:

Start   Finish   Total

Fuel level   Water level

No of miles   No of locks

Weather

Waterway conditions

Purpose of journey

Notes

Places passed

Other boats seen

Wildlife seen

Details of mooring

Jobs done

Jobs to do

Daily Pages

Date/day

Waterway

From   To

Crew on board

Guests

Start time   Finish

Engine hours:

Start   Finish   Total

Fuel level   Water level

No of miles   No of locks

Weather

Waterway conditions

Purpose of journey

Notes

Places passed

Other boats seen

Wildlife seen

Details of mooring

Jobs done

Jobs to do

Date/day

Waterway

From   To

Crew on board

Guests

Start time   Finish

Engine hours:

Start   Finish   Total

Fuel level   Water level

No of miles   No of locks

Weather

Waterway conditions

Purpose of journey

Notes

Places passed

Other boats seen

Wildlife seen

Details of mooring

Jobs done

Jobs to do

Date/day

Waterway

From   To

Crew on board

Guests

Start time   Finish

Engine hours:

Start   Finish   Total

Fuel level   Water level

No of miles   No of locks

Weather

Waterway conditions

Purpose of journey

Notes

Places passed

Other boats seen

Wildlife seen

Details of mooring

Jobs done

Jobs to do

Date/day

Waterway

From   To

Crew on board

Guests

Start time   Finish

Engine hours:

Start   Finish   Total

Fuel level   Water level

No of miles   No of locks

Weather

Waterway conditions

Purpose of journey

Notes

Places passed

Other boats seen

Wildlife seen

Details of mooring

Jobs done

Jobs to do

Date/day

Waterway

From _____ To

Crew on board

Guests

Start time _____ Finish

Engine hours:

Start _____ Finish _____ Total

Fuel level _____ Water level

No of miles _____ No of locks

Weather

Waterway conditions

Purpose of journey

Notes

Places passed

Other boats seen

Wildlife seen

Details of mooring

Jobs done

Jobs to do

Date/day

Waterway

From _____ To

Crew on board

Guests

Start time _____ Finish

Engine hours:

Start _____ Finish _____ Total

Fuel level _____ Water level

No of miles _____ No of locks

Weather

Waterway conditions

Purpose of journey

Notes

Places passed

Other boats seen

Wildlife seen

Details of mooring

Jobs done

Jobs to do

Date/day

Waterway

From   To

Crew on board

Guests

Start time   Finish

Engine hours:

Start   Finish   Total

Fuel level   Water level

No of miles   No of locks

Weather

Waterway conditions

Purpose of journey

Notes

Places passed

Other boats seen

Wildlife seen

Details of mooring

Jobs done

Jobs to do

Daily Pages

Date/day

Waterway

From   To

Crew on board

Guests

Start time   Finish

Engine hours:

Start   Finish   Total

Fuel level   Water level

No of miles   No of locks

Weather

Waterway conditions

Purpose of journey

Notes

Places passed

Other boats seen

Wildlife seen

Details of mooring

Jobs done

Jobs to do

Date/day

Waterway

From   To

Crew on board

Guests

Start time   Finish

Engine hours:

Start   Finish   Total

Fuel level   Water level

No of miles   No of locks

Weather

Waterway conditions

Purpose of journey

Notes

Places passed

Other boats seen

Wildlife seen

Details of mooring

Jobs done

Jobs to do

Daily Pages

Date/day

Waterway

From   To

Crew on board

Guests

Start time   Finish

Engine hours:

Start   Finish   Total

Fuel level   Water level

No of miles   No of locks

Weather

Waterway conditions

Purpose of journey

Notes

Places passed

Other boats seen

Wildlife seen

Details of mooring

Jobs done

Jobs to do

Date/day

Waterway

From _____ To

Crew on board

Guests

Start time _____ Finish

Engine hours:

Start _____ Finish _____ Total

Fuel level _____ Water level

No of miles _____ No of locks

Weather

Waterway conditions

Purpose of journey

Notes

Places passed

Other boats seen

Wildlife seen

Details of mooring

Jobs done

Jobs to do

Daily Pages

Date/day

Waterway _____

From _____ To _____

Crew on board _____

Guests _____

Start time _____ Finish _____

Engine hours:

Start _____ Finish _____ Total _____

Fuel level _____ Water level _____

No of miles _____ No of locks _____

Weather _____

Waterway conditions _____

Purpose of journey _____

_____

_____

_____

_____

Notes

Places passed _____

_____

_____

_____

_____

Other boats seen _____

_____

Wildlife seen _____

_____

Details of mooring _____

_____

Jobs done _____

Jobs to do _____

Date/day

Waterway

From ___ To

Crew on board

Guests

Start time ___ Finish

Engine hours:

Start ___ Finish ___ Total

Fuel level ___ Water level

No of miles ___ No of locks

Weather

Waterway conditions

Purpose of journey

Notes

Places passed

Other boats seen

Wildlife seen

Details of mooring

Jobs done

Jobs to do

Date/day

Waterway

From   To

Crew on board

Guests

Start time   Finish

Engine hours:

Start   Finish   Total

Fuel level   Water level

No of miles   No of locks

Weather

Waterway conditions

Purpose of journey

Notes

Places passed

Other boats seen

Wildlife seen

Details of mooring

Jobs done

Jobs to do

Date/day

Waterway

From   To

Crew on board

Guests

Start time   Finish

Engine hours:

Start   Finish   Total

Fuel level   Water level

No of miles   No of locks

Weather

Waterway conditions

Purpose of journey

Notes

Places passed

Other boats seen

Wildlife seen

Details of mooring

Jobs done

Jobs to do

Daily Pages

Date/day

Waterway

From   To

Crew on board

Guests

Start time   Finish

Engine hours:

Start   Finish   Total

Fuel level   Water level

No of miles   No of locks

Weather

Waterway conditions

Purpose of journey

Notes

Places passed

Other boats seen

Wildlife seen

Details of mooring

Jobs done

Jobs to do

Date/day

Waterway

From   To

Crew on board

Guests

Start time   Finish

Engine hours:

Start   Finish   Total

Fuel level   Water level

No of miles   No of locks

Weather

Waterway conditions

Purpose of journey

Notes

Places passed

Other boats seen

Wildlife seen

Details of mooring

Jobs done

Jobs to do

Date/day

Waterway

From   To

Crew on board

Guests

Start time   Finish

Engine hours:

Start   Finish   Total

Fuel level   Water level

No of miles   No of locks

Weather

Waterway conditions

Purpose of journey

Notes

Places passed

Other boats seen

Wildlife seen

Details of mooring

Jobs done

Jobs to do

Date/day

Waterway

From   To

Crew on board

Guests

Start time   Finish

Engine hours:

Start   Finish   Total

Fuel level   Water level

No of miles   No of locks

Weather

Waterway conditions

Purpose of journey

Notes

Places passed

Other boats seen

Wildlife seen

Details of mooring

Jobs done

Jobs to do

Date/day

Waterway

From   To

Crew on board

Guests

Start time   Finish

Engine hours:

Start   Finish   Total

Fuel level   Water level

No of miles   No of locks

Weather

Waterway conditions

Purpose of journey

Notes

Places passed

Other boats seen

Wildlife seen

Details of mooring

Jobs done

Jobs to do

Useful Addresses

Guests

Published by Adlard Coles Nautical
an imprint of A & C Black Publishers Ltd
36 Soho Square, London W1D 3QY
www.adlardcoles.com

First edition published 2009

ISBN 978-1-4081-1203-8

A CIP catalogue record for this book is available from the British Library.

This book is produced using paper that is made from wood grown in managed, sustainable forests. It is natural, renewable and recyclable. The logging and manufacturing processes conform to the environmental regulations of the country of origin.

Design by Fred Barter at Bosun Press

Typeset in 10pt Rockwell
Printed and bound in Spain by GraphyCems